Topic 1

The British Constitution

The UK's constitutional arrangements

A constitution is a .... principles that set out how a state functions. This could be in the form of a single codified document (e.g. the US constitution, which has seven articles and 27 amendments) or be uncodified, taking the form of a compilation of documents from a variety of sources (e.g. the UK's constitution). Three key functions of constitutions are:

- to set out the distribution of power within a state
- to outline the rights of citizens
- to explain the political processes — such as the working of elections or the terms of office of elected representatives — that support the state

What is the nature of the UK's constitution?

The traditional constitution of the UK is regarded as being simple and straightforward in its form. The arrangements are often referred to as the Westminster model — a form of government which emphasises the efficiency of a sovereign parliament, governing within a highly centralised political system with fused executive and legislative powers. Supporters of such relatively extraordinary arrangements identify several key characteristics.

---

1 What is a *constitution*? (AO1)   `2 marks`

....

....

2 Complete the following table with explanations and comparisons similar to the ones given, comparing the UK and US constitutions. (AO1, AO2 & AO3)   `6 marks`

UK constitution characteristic	Explanation and example	US comparison
Uncodified	Not one single document but drawn together from a series of documents and principles developed over several centuries. The Bill of Rights (1689) sits alongside the House of Lords Act (1999)	
Flexible		Constitutionally rigid — just 27 amendments in well over two centuries
Unentrenched		
Fused powers		

3 Briefly explain the term *separation of powers* (compare the UK to the USA). (AO1) `4 marks`

....

....

....

....

4 Using examples, explain the difference between *flexible* and *rigid* constitutions. (A01) `4 marks`

....

....

....

....

5 Why is the UK's constitution referred to as being *uncodified* but not unwritten? (AO1, AO2 & AO3) `10 marks`

Write your answer on a separate sheet and keep it with your workbook for reference.

Sources and principles

What are the sources of the UK's constitution?

6 The UK's uncodified constitution draws its explanations, processes and principles from a wide variety of sources. Complete the following table. (AO1, AO2 & AO3) `6 marks`

Source	Explanation	Example
Statute law	The most significant body of constitutional documents take the form of Acts of Parliament which set out such things as the powers of the regional assemblies, the basic rights of citizens and the functioning of Parliament	
Common law		
Conventions		

Source	Explanation	Example
Royal prerogatives		Waging war, signing treaties, appointing or dismissing ministers
External constitutional agreements		
Works of authority		

7 **What is the *royal prerogative*? (AO1)** `2 marks`

> TIP   Visit **www.tinyurl.com/p54d6no** for detailed information on the royal prerogative.

....

....

....

8 **Explain the term *works of authority*. (AO1)** `2 marks`

....

....

....

9 **Explain the significance of three sources of the UK's constitution. (AO1, AO2 & AO3)** `10 marks`

Write your answer on a separate sheet and keep it with your workbook for reference.

What are the principles on which the UK's constitution is based?

Principle	Explanation	Example
Parliamentary sovereignty	There is no higher authority than Parliament. Parliament can change the constitutional arrangements of the state at will	The House of Lords Act (1999) swept away a thousand years of history by removing all but 92 hereditary peers. It was passed the same way as other Acts
Rule of law	A. V. Dicey asserted that the rule of law was a central feature of any democratic state. Everyone is subject to and equal before the law; everyone is entitled to a fair trial	Control orders, e.g. placing strict conditions on the liberty of suspected terrorists, within the Prevention of Terrorism Act (2005) are said by many to undermine the principles of the rule of law
Parliamentary government	The prime minister, ministers and the government depend on Parliament for their support. They are accountable to Parliament which is at the centre of the political system	Prime Minister's Questions take place every Wednesday when Parliament is in session and are an example of Parliament holding the executive to account
Unitary state	All political power is concentrated at the centre; there is no sharing of sovereignty between elements of the state as under a federal system	In theory the UK Parliament could withdraw devolved powers and close down regional assemblies, as Margaret Thatcher did to the Greater London Council, which was dissolved by the Local Government Act in 1986

10 Explain how *parliamentary government* differs from *presidential government*. (AO1) `4 marks`

....

....

....

....

11 Explain the term *rule of law*. (AO1) `5 marks`

....

....

....

....

....

....

12 What is the difference between *unitary* and *federal systems*? (AO1, AO2 & AO3) `10 marks`

Write your answer on a separate sheet and keep it with your workbook for reference.

Constitutional reform 1997 to present

New Labour and constitutional change (1997–2010)

13 Constitutional reforms under New Labour were wide ranging. Complete the following table with explanations and examples of the four broad themes that characterised New Labour's constitutional changes. (AO1, AO2 & AO3) `6 marks`

Theme	Explanation	Example
Decentralisation	Ensuring that government decision making and accountability is closer to the citizens affected	
Democratisation		AMS in Scotland and the closed regional lists system for EU elections
Modernisation		
Enhancing rights		

⑭ Outline and explain three advantages of the constitutional reforms brought in by New Labour between 1997 and 2010. (AO1)

6 marks

....

....

....

....

....

....

....

The coalition government and constitutional change (2010–)

Constitutional reform became a significant feature of the deal that saw the coalition partners come together to form a government in 2010. In the event, the Liberal Democrat agenda has largely been thwarted:

- Electoral reform is off the agenda following the rejection of the alternative vote in May 2011.
- Reforms to the House of Lords have been postponed after Nick Clegg's 300-strong second chamber was rejected.
- The findings of a commission to investigate the creation of a British Bill of Rights resulted in no change to the Human Rights Act.

Should the UK codify its constitutional arrangements?

Yes	No
• A codified constitution would provide much needed clarity in times of unpredictability or crisis. • Codification would check and balance executive power. • Rights would be entrenched within a codified constitution. • Codification would bring the UK's political system into line with other modern democracies.	• The current constitutional arrangements 'work'. • Effective checks and balances do exist. • Codification would not enhance democracy — instead handing power to unelected judges. • On a practical level, codification is unachievable.

Exam-style questions

The need for constitutional change

In the second half of the twentieth century the UK's uncodified constitution came under intense pressure amid growing social and economic pressures. EU membership and further integration led to conflict over the compromising of parliamentary sovereignty. The growth in prime ministerial power appeared to undermine collegial cabinet government. The rise of 'quangos' and the onset of privatisation blurred traditional lines of government accountability. The decline of trust in politicians and the rise of sleaze among them fuelled criticisms of the UK's traditional, informal constitutional arrangements — arrangements that appeared to have failed to check the growth of executive power.

15 Explain the term *uncodified constitution* used in the extract. (AO1) `5 marks` (5)

16 Using your own knowledge as well as the extract, outline and explain at least two criticisms of the UK's traditional constitutional arrangements. (AO1, AO2 & AO3) `10 marks` (10)

17 To what extent should the UK reform its constitution in favour of a codified alternative? (AO1, AO2 & AO3) `25 marks` (30)

Rights and the judicial system

Rights and the law

Human rights	Civil rights
Fundamental freedoms — such as the right to life or freedom from torture — that all human beings should enjoy	Basic freedoms granted to individuals within liberal democracies. They may vary from state to state and may be limited in times of national emergency or war
Criminal law	**Civil law**
Laws that deal with serious crimes against the state, e.g. violent crime and burglary, usually punishable by a prison sentence	Laws relating to relationships — between individuals or individuals and organisations — usually connected to legal contracts

The UK judiciary

The UK judiciary is often represented as a pyramid structure to reflect a judicial hierarchy from lay magistrates at the bottom, who apply the law to lesser crimes, to Court of Appeal judges and Supreme Court justices at the top who have the power to set legal precedent by clarifying the meaning of the law, thereby establishing common law.

18 What are *rights*? (AO1) `2 marks`

....

....

19 Briefly explain the significance of the *UK Supreme Court*. (AO1) `4 marks`

> **TIP** Visit **www.supremecourt.gov.uk** and click on *About the Supreme Court* then *Role of the Supreme Court*.

....

....

....

....

....

....

20 Explain the term *common law*. (AO1)

5 marks

....

....

....

....

The judiciary: change and reform

Several significant changes or reforms to the British judiciary have occurred within the last 10 years.

EU membership

- Britain's membership of the European Union (following the European Communities Act, 1972) incorporated the Treaty of Rome into British law, giving precedence to European law where the two conflicted.
- The Factortame case in 1990 set the precedent for EU predominance. The UK Merchant Shipping Act of 1988 was set aside as it discriminated against Spanish fishermen.

The Human Rights Act (HRA)

The Human Rights Act (1998, coming into force in 2000) incorporated the European Convention on Human Rights (ECHR) into British domestic law. This had two major consequences:

- where aggrieved British citizens had previously sought redress through the European Court of Human Rights in Strasbourg they could now pursue cases under the ECHR through British courts
- all institutions below Parliament — which itself declared an intention to ensure legislative

compatibility with the ECHR — would be bound by the ECHR

The Constitutional Reform Act (CRA), 2005

The CRA brought in three major changes to the structure and functioning of the British judiciary:

- In 2006 the **Judicial Appointments Committee** was created. An independent panel of experts was appointed to replace appointment by 'secret soundings' and broaden the social mix of senior judicial appointments.
- In 2006 the role of the **Lord Chancellor** was dismantled. Previously spanning the separation of power (as head of the judiciary, Speaker of the Lords and a cabinet minister), responsibilities were split between the Home Office and the Ministry of Justice. The Lord Chancellor is now responsible for the functioning of the legal system as Secretary of State for Justice.
- In October 2009 the **UK Supreme Court** was created from 11 of the 12 former Law Lords. It separated the judicial from the legislative branch and acted as the final court of appeal in England, Wales and Northern Ireland.

21 What is the significance of the *Factortame* case? (AO1)

4 marks

....

....

....

....

22 Briefly explain why the *European Convention on Human Rights* has become more significant in the UK in recent years. (AO1) `4 marks`

....

....

....

....

23 Explain how the *Human Rights Act* has affected the operation of the British judiciary. (AO1, AO2 & AO3) `10 marks`

> **TIP** Visit **www.tinyurl.com/qyc2um7** for examples of declarations made since the Human Rights Act was enacted.

....

....

....

....

....

....

....

....

....

....

Judicial independence and neutrality

A significant element of liberal democracy is a judicial system entirely free from political control or partisanship, able to protect the rights of citizens from government abuse and ensure that checks on government power are effective.

Judicial independence

Judicial independence is maintained in these ways:
- The CRA created an independent appointments panel to ensure that these were not subject to political interference or favouritism.
- Judges have security of tenure meaning that once appointed they cannot be dismissed unless for misconduct.
- Judicial salaries are paid from the 'consolidated fund', protected from government interference.
- When a case is being heard it is *sub judice* forbidding anyone from commenting.

Judicial neutrality

Judicial neutrality refers to the importance of judges acting impartially when passing judgements — not favouring one element of society over others. In the UK:
- Judges are required to have no affiliation with political parties.
- The rule of law — equality before and under the law and the right to a fair trial — are prime features of the judicial system.
- While a trial is in process, details are *sub judice*, meaning that no politicians or commentators can express opinions.

24 'Neither independent nor neutral.' To what extent is this an accurate statement about the UK's judiciary? (AO1, AO2 & AO3)

25 marks

Plan your answer in the space below and then write your essay on a separate sheet of paper.

How effective is the UK's judiciary?

Two key areas of evaluation regularly emerge when considering the effectiveness of the judiciary:

- the ability of the judicial branch to check government power
- the effectiveness of the courts in upholding or protecting the civil liberties of ordinary citizens

Checking the power of the government

The power of judicial review allows senior members of the judiciary to challenge decisions or policies made by the state. The grounds for judicial review might be:

- A minister or agent of the state has acted *ultra vires* — beyond their assigned powers.
- Legislation or actions are incompatible with the Human Rights Act (even though parliamentary legislation may not be overturned on this basis by the courts).
- Correct judicial protocol has not been followed in the application of justice.

The power (or threat) of judicial review is significant in checking government power and making agents of the state more attuned to the expectations of the rule of law.

25 Outline and explain the significance of judicial review. (AO1, AO2 & AO3)

10 marks

Protecting rights and liberties of citizens

The courts protect civil liberties in a number of ways. They can overturn decisions that have infringed an individual's human rights (under the ECHR), set new precedents in common law to take account of new threats to liberties and enforce parliamentary statutes that protect liberties with greater rigour in the face of government attacks.

Do the courts protect civil liberties effectively?

Yes	No
• The body of anti-discrimination legislation has grown in recent decades — liberties guarded by statutes are more easily protected. • The Human Rights Act has added greater clarity to the protection of liberties. • Judicial reforms in recent years have served to enhance the legitimacy of the judges in challenging other branches. • Cases of judicial review have grown, illustrating a greater willingness on the part of judges to check state power.	• Parliament is not bound by the ECHR and has been known to ignore recommendations (e.g. control orders in the Prevention of Terrorism Act) that infringe it. • Legislation to curtail rights, e.g. the Regulation of Investigatory Powers Act (2000) and the Civil Contingencies Act (2004), has undermined liberties in a way that judges cannot challenge. • The courts are limited in the scope of their protective duties by the fact that appeals need to be launched by redress-seeking individuals.

Exam-style questions

The creation of the UK Supreme Court addressed several pressing constitutional concerns, most notably the relationship between the judicial branch and the legislature. The creation of a separate physical entity has enhanced the visibility of the role and significance of the highest UK court of appeal but the prospect of judges becoming policy makers — similar to their US counterparts — is remote. The UK's uncodified constitution, sustained by the principle of parliamentary sovereignty, means that the judicial role remains an interpretative one.

26 Explain the term *parliamentary sovereignty*, used in the extract. (AO1)　　　5 marks　　5

....

....

....

....

Write your answers on a separate sheet and keep it with your workbook for reference.

27 Using your own knowledge as well as the extract, explain how the creation of a UK Supreme Court changed the relationship between judicial, executive and legislative branches. (AO1, AO2 & AO3)　　　10 marks　　10

28 How effective are judges in protecting the rights and liberties of UK citizens? (AO1, AO2 & AO3)　　　25 marks　　30

Topic 2
Parliament

The composition and functions of the Commons and Lords

The principles of parliamentary sovereignty and parliamentary government mean that Parliament is at the centre of political activity in the UK. The UK Parliament is bicameral which means that it has two chambers. The way that it functions as well as the way that it is made up have been key issues since 1997.

> **1** What is *bicameralism*? (AO1)   `2 marks`
>
> TIP   Visit **www.tinyurl.com/nffewdk** for a comparison with the US Congress.
>
> ....
>
> ....

The composition of Parliament

House of Commons:
- 650 MPs each representing a constituency — a geographic area with roughly 70,000 voters.
- The largest party forms the government or is the leading partner in a coalition government.
- Leading figures in government or shadow cabinet are known as frontbenchers; other MPs are known as backbenchers.

House of Lords:
- Lords Temporal: currently 650 life peers and 92 hereditary peers; life peers are appointed by the monarch on the advice of the prime minister, hereditary peers inherit their titles.
- Lords Spiritual: 26 archbishops and bishops.
- Crossbenchers: over 200 peers that are not affiliated to any party.

Party affiliation

Party	House of Commons*	House of Lords
Conservative	306	209
Labour	258	217
Liberal Democrat	57	89
Other	31	13
Crossbenchers	n/a	205
Lords Spiritual	n/a	26
Total	650	759

* following the 2010 general election

> **2** Using examples, explain the term *backbencher*. (AO1)   `2 marks`
>
> ....
>
> ....

13

3 Explain an advantage of having each of the following groups in the House of Lords. (AO1)

6 marks

Hereditary peers

....

....

Lords Spiritual

....

....

Crossbenchers

....

....

4 Explain the term *life peer*. (AO1)

3 marks

....

....

....

....

....

The functions of Parliament

Most parliamentary functions are shared between the two houses. However, while the House of Lords is traditionally referred to as the 'upper house', it is the House of Commons that is the dominant partner. The key functions are:

- **Representation:** the primary function of Parliament is to act as the nation's representative assembly. The Commons represents the specific interests of constituencies and constituents, and the Lords can be seen to represent a wide range of causes and other interests.
- **Legislation:** both houses are involved in the passage of legislation. The vast majority of bills are government-backed and originate in the Commons, but the expertise in the House of Lords improves and amends most legislation and can delay it for up to a year.
- **Scrutiny:** both houses are responsible for holding the government to account. Parliamentary committees in both houses scrutinise the performance of the government. The Commons has the ultimate power of removing a government through a vote of no confidence.
- **Other:** MPs in the Commons seek redress for aggrieved constituents. Both houses provide a forum for debating and voting on key issues and a training ground for future ministerial positions.

5 Using examples, explain the term *government accountability*. (AO1)

4 marks

....

....

....

....

6 Identify and explain three ways in which the functions of the House of Commons differ from those of the House of Lords. (AO1, AO2 & AO3)   6 marks

1 ....

....

2 ....

....

3 ....

....

How representative is Parliament?

There are two elements to any analysis of Parliament's representative function. Does the composition of Parliament represent the wider population of the UK (resemblance theory) and does it matter?

Representation and the Commons

The Commons is not representative of the population of the UK in several key areas:

- **Gender:** the representation of women has improved significantly but only 22% of MPs elected in 2010 were women (up from 19% in 2005). There are currently 147 female MPs.
- **Age:** the average age of MPs elected in 2010 is 50. Ages ranged in 2014 from the oldest MP at 84 (Sir Peter Tapsell, Conservative) to the youngest at 29 (Pamela Nash, Labour).

- **Ethnicity and religion:** the 2010 general election returned 27 MPs from ethnic minorities (4%). It also saw the number of Muslim MPs doubling to eight. Despite this the Commons remains a disproportionately white/Christian chamber.

While an unrepresentative chamber can be argued to lack an effective, legitimate mandate, the reality is that constituents will always be represented by people unlike them. The role of an MP is to represent all constituents regardless of ethnicity, faith or gender. Many MPs work tirelessly to further the interests of minorities and disadvantaged groups in their constituencies.

7 Outline and explain the significance of the term *mandate*. (AO1)   4 marks

....

....

....

....

8 Explain the term *resemblance theory*. (AO1)   5 marks

....

....

....

....

15

Representation and the Lords

The House of Lords experienced radical change following the House of Lords Act (1999) when all but 92 hereditary peers were removed from the chamber. The previous 'in-built Tory majority' was eradicated since the vast majority of hereditary peers were Conservative (471 to Labour's 179). The large number of Labour life peers appointed after 1999 redressed the party balance.

Despite being unelected and unrepresentative (there are nearly three times the number of male life peers to female life peers) the Lords is praised for its inclusion of experts in the fields of human rights, science, business and innovation, health and education and the armed forces. However, it is still seen as being socially elite and lacks any form of accountability.

The appointment of life peers

The Life Peerages Act (1958) was designed to revive an Upper House seen as out of touch with a rapidly changing society. Although appointments are made by the monarch, the prime minister — on the advice of the House of Lords Appointments Commission — has a great deal of autonomy.

The process has been the subject of controversy as several prime ministers have appointed peers specifically to include them in their governments (e.g. Gordon Brown ennobled Peter Mandelson in 2009 and made him Secretary of State for Business, Innovation and Skills), while others have ennobled major party donors.

9 Outline and explain two advantages and two disadvantages of *appointed peers.* (AO1, AO2 & AO3) **8 marks**

....
....
....
....
....
....
....
....
....
....

10 How well does Parliament perform its representative function? (AO1, AO2 & AO3) **25 marks**

Plan your answer in the space below and then write your essay on a separate sheet of paper.

....
....
....
....
....
....
....
....
....

Parliamentary sovereignty vs elective dictatorship

Parliamentary sovereignty is identified as one of the twin pillars of the UK's constitution. In theory, Parliament is supreme: it can make or abolish any law and is not bound by any other body, including previous parliaments.

In practice however, commentators maintain that while legislative sovereignty remains with Parliament, on a day-to-day basis real power — political sovereignty — lies with the executive. The lack of a separation of powers allows the executive to dominate Parliament (all members of the executive are within the legislature) and the prevalence of large electoral majorities has prompted some — most notably Lord Hailsham in 1974 — to warn of 'elective dictatorship'.

The process of devolution of power to the regions, the surrendering of sovereignty to the European Union — where UK and EU laws conflict, EU laws are supreme — and the wider use of referendums have contributed to the erosion of parliamentary sovereignty.

11 **Using examples, explain the term *elective dictatorship*. (AO1)** `4 marks`

....
....
....
....

12 **Where does sovereignty lie in the UK? (AO1, AO2 & AO3)** `8 marks`

....
....
....
....
....
....
....
....

How effectively does Parliament hold the government to account?

What methods does Parliament use to scrutinise the executive?

There are several ways that Parliament can scrutinise the work of the government, thereby holding it to account. One of the most prominent is the work of committees. Other ways include Prime Minister's Questions (which take place every Wednesday for 30 minutes) and regular ministers' questions, examination by the official opposition (there are 20 days allocated per parliamentary session), through the expertise of the House of Lords, various backbenchers (often via Early Day Motions) and the ultimate way of holding a government to account — a vote of no confidence.

13 Explain two ways that *Prime Minister's Questions* in the House of Commons is significant. (AO1)

`3 marks`

....

....

....

14 Complete the following table to explain and exemplify the role of committees in the House of Commons. (AO1, AO2 & AO3)

`6 marks`

Type of committee	Explanation (including analysis of strengths and weaknesses)	Example
Select committees		
Public bill committee		

In what ways does the government dominate Parliament?

A combination of a lack of separation of powers which allows the executive to be part of the legislature, a majoritarian electoral system that usually presents governments with over-large majorities and an uncodified constitution whereby no clear understanding of the distribution of power exists make it hardly surprising that the government is able to dominate Parliament.

15 Complete the following table to explain and exemplify the key ways that Parliament is dominated by the executive. (AO1, AO2 & AO3)

`10 marks`

Method of domination	Explanation	Example
Prime ministerial patronage		
Culture of party loyalty		
Power of party whips		

The legislative process

Two types of bills exist:

- **Public bills.** These are either government bills (usually contained within a manifesto, supported by the government and invariably passed into law) or Private Members' Bills (originating with individual MPs and usually doomed to fail unless receiving government backing).

- **Private bills.** These are specific and affect certain individuals or organisations and not the general public.

While some bills sail through each stage, others are beset by difficulties and delays. Tactics such as whipped votes and guillotine motions to curtail debate can be countered by the Lords power of delay of up to a year.

---

16 **What is a *Private Member's Bill*? (AO1)** `2 marks`

> **TIP** Visit **www.tinyurl.com/np4n5jy** to find out more.

....

....

17 **Briefly explain the stages of the legislative process. (AO1, AO2 & AO3)** `10 marks`

> **TIP** Visit **www.tinyurl.com/23nj25n** for help.

| Preparation (Green Paper) |
| First reading |
| Second reading |
| Committee stage |
| Report stage |
| Third reading |
| Lords stages |
| Royal assent |

The less partisan character of the House of Lords ensures that it is often seen as a place of genuine debate and effective, informed criticism of government activity. The strength of having experts involved in the legislative process is widely acknowledged and this only serves to enhance the legitimacy of the laws generated. In times of weak Commons opposition — such as 1997–2005 — the Lords can be a potent check on government power.

18 **Outline and explain the significance of the *Salisbury Doctrine*. (AO1)**   `4 marks`

....

....

....

....

....

19 **Outline and explain three factors that limit the House of Lords checking the power of the House of Commons. (AO1, AO2 & AO3)**   `6 marks`

....

....

....

....

....

....

....

....

....

....

....

....

The process of House of Lords reform

There have been three distinct phases in the process of reform to the House of Lords:

- **1997–99: House of Lords Act (1999).** The frustrations of the Labour Party in opposition together with an acknowledgement that at over 1,300 members the Lords was cumbersome and ineffective saw the removal of all but 92 hereditary peers in a 'transitional house', a key element of New Labour's constitutional reforms.

- **1999–2010: stalled reform.** Commissions and White Papers detailing various proportions of elected and appointed peers led to vague Labour manifesto commitments in 2001 and 2005, subsequent free votes in the Commons and Lords but no further progress in settling the size and nature of the second chamber.

- **2010–present: reform renewed.** Parliamentary reform features high on the Liberal Democrat agenda and Lords reform was a bargaining chip in the original coalition agreement in 2010 but Conservative support for a fully elected second chamber has yet to be forthcoming.

20 Complete the following table to explain the various options for future reform of the House of Lords. (AO1, AO2 & AO3))

8 marks

Option	Argument for	Argument against
Abolition of the second chamber		
A fully appointed second chamber		
A fully elected second chamber		
A partly elected and partly appointed second chamber		

Exam-style questions

MPs are rightly praised for their commitment to furthering the interests of their constituents. Additionally, the work of many backbench MPs in highlighting the deficiencies of government departments through select committee work is increasingly understood and often highly effective. However, lacking research expertise and time, the culture of party loyalty and the power of the whips often overwhelms even the most independently-minded of backbenchers.

It is often peers that provide much-needed expertise in improving legislation and challenging government activity. But without the much-needed democratic legitimacy of elections their impact remains limited.

21 Explain the term *select committee* used in the extract. (AO1) 5 marks ⏱ 5

....

....

....

....

22 Using your own knowledge as well as the extract, outline three arguments in favour of a fully elected second chamber. (AO1, AO2 & AO3) 10 marks ⏱ 10

....

....

....

....

....

....

....

....

....

....

23 How effective is Parliament in holding the government to account? (AO1, AO2 & AO3) 25 marks ⏱ 25

Use the space below to construct a detailed plan and then write the full answer an a separate sheet of paper.

....

....

....

....

....

....

....

....

....

....

Topic 3
The core executive

The UK's changing executive

The core executive is the focus for political power in the UK. The relationships between the elements that comprise it — the prime minister, ministers and civil servants — have long been the subject of debate and discussion. Factors that have blurred traditional lines of consultation and decision making include:

- the centralisation of power in the hands of the prime minister
- the growing complexity of government, especially under a coalition government
- the ever-shifting nature of political communication
- the rise of special advisers, independent of the permanent civil service

1 **Briefly explain the composition of the *core executive*. (AO1)** `2 marks`

....

....

2 **What is *coalition government*? (AO1)** `2 marks`

....

....

....

3 **Research and explain the difference between *special advisers* and *civil servants*? (AO1)** `3 marks`

....

....

....

The British prime minister: powers and constraints

Prime ministerial power

The British prime minister is head of the government, holding a post that has emerged and developed over several centuries. The evolution of the role and the absence of a codified constitution mean that there is no definitive list of responsibilities. However, such ambiguity is not unique to the UK — a number of significant presidential roles in the USA have developed by convention — and several key responsibilities can be identified.

4 Complete the following table to explain the key powers of the prime minister. Provide a relevant contemporary example where possible. `8 marks`

Power	Explanation
Power of appointment ('hiring and firing')	
Directing the government	Setting policy objectives, short- and long-term strategic goals and determining the cabinet agenda are key prime ministerial responsibilities. While these are determined and achieved in conjunction with cabinet colleagues, the premier's personal role in policy making and agenda setting is formidable.
Managing Parliament	
National and international leadership	

5 How significant are the *patronage powers* of the British prime minister? (AO1, AO2 & AO3) `10 marks`

Constraints on a prime minister: the six Ps

The rise of the mass media and the centralisation of decision making have strengthened the British premier but there remain several notable constraints on prime ministerial power.

1 *Primus inter pares.* Literally meaning 'first among equals'. An effective **cabinet** will balance wings or factions of the party and will contain senior figures that may not be natural allies of the premier. Ignoring, marginalising or dominating the cabinet can lead to criticism. High-profile resignations can be damaging. Margaret Thatcher lost the support of her party and the public, but it was the loss of cabinet support that precipitated her departure.

2 **Party.** Controlling the largest party in the Commons is vital, so the prospect of rebellions can affect a prime minister's agenda. Sustained backbench criticism irreversibly undermined Gordon Brown in the run-up to 2010.

3 **Parliament.** The accountability function of Parliament requires the PM to face weekly questioning and be subject to the scrutiny of select committees. Legislative defeat can be harmful to a PM's reputation. David Cameron's first major Commons defeat — on EU spending in October 2012 — prompted a change of policy over Europe.

4 **People.** Damaging opinion poll data, defeats in by-elections or disappointing local election performances can provide a significant check on prime ministerial power. The 'revolt of the shires' (local elections, May 2013) was said to be 'humbling' for the Conservative prime minister.

5 **Personal qualities.** Herbert Asquith's observation that 'the office of the prime minister is what its holder chooses and is able to make of it' remains relevant today. Charismatic leaders are often less likely to face challenges or defeats.

6 **Political circumstances.** Healthy Commons majorities — such as those enjoyed by Tony Blair between 1997 and 2005 — allow a premier to appear more effective and decisive. 'Events, dear boy. Events' is Harold Macmillan's explanation of the ebb and flow of prime ministerial power. Foreign wars or economic crises present unforeseen opportunities for a prime minister to lead the way or appear incompetent.

---

6 Explain the term *primus inter pares.* (AO1)   2 marks

....

....

7 Briefly explain how *political circumstances* can influence prime ministerial power. (AO1)   2 marks

....

....

8 Outline and explain three constraints on a prime minister's power. (AO1, AO2 & AO3)   10 marks

....

....

....

....

....

....

....

....

....

....

....

The British prime minister: too powerful or presidential?

The arguments over the extent to which the British prime minister has become *too powerful* should not be confused with those that address whether he or she has become *presidential*. Although both share similar evidence and examples, the former analyses powers and constraints within a contemporary setting; the latter reflects on the nature of presidentialism and evaluates the changing role and status of the prime minister.

Is the British prime minister too powerful?

9 **Complete the following table by adding explanations and examples.**   8 marks

Yes, the British prime minister is too powerful	
Power	**Explanation and example**
Appoints and dismisses ministers	
Controls cabinet agenda	
Leads largest party	
Enjoys high public profile	

No, the British prime minister is not too powerful	
Constraint	**Explanation and example**
Restricted by cabinet personnel	
Limited by Parliament	
Challenged by party	
Blamed for policy failure	

Has the British prime minister become presidential?

The predominance of the prime minister has led many to conclude that the position is 'presidential' in all but name. The cultivation of **spacial leadership** — placing the role above party political contests — has become a key stylistic device of modern prime ministers.

> **10** 'The British prime minister has become a president in all but name.'
> **Discuss. (AO1, AO2 & AO3)**   `25 marks`
>
> TIP Four key areas to include:
> - Introduce **key similarities and differences** with specific examples and defined roles.
> - Research Michael Foley's 1993 text *The Rise of the British Presidency* online or in your textbook. Outline **how the British prime minister is said to have become more presidential.**
> - Explain **how a British prime minister might be considered more or less powerful than a US president** with examples.
> - Develop the **'more style than substance'** argument with examples.
>
> **Write your answer on a separate sheet and keep it with your workbook for reference.**

The British cabinet: organisation and function

Like the office of prime minister, the British cabinet has evolved over several centuries. It has been celebrated for its role in connecting the key elements of the governing process — referred to by Walter Bagehot as 'the hyphen which joins, a buckle which fastens the legislative part of the state to the executive part of the state'.

Cabinet organisation

- Modern cabinets comprise around 22–23 senior government figures (cabinet ministers) responsible for the key departments of state.
- The complexity of government decision making means that most decisions are ratified rather than discussed by the cabinet.
- Cabinet committees are where most decisions are made. Committees might comprise the prime minister and specific departmental ministers to cover key areas of foreign, home and economic affairs.
- The Cabinet Office (CO) is central to government decision making, coordinating the working of a vast array of government departments and personnel.

The growth of the CO in recent years has provided the prime minister with the resources (around 2,000 staff) to be more active in departmental affairs.

Cabinet function

The cabinet performs a number of key roles in the political system:
- **Legitimising government decision making.** The cabinet formalises government policy and is collectively bound by all government decisions (even ones taken in cabinet committees or elsewhere).
- **Resolving and coordinating policy.** Although the formulation of policy rarely takes place at cabinet level, the cabinet is the forum for ironing out departmental conflicts, determining the coherent presentation of policy and allocating appropriate funds.
- **Crisis management.** When emergencies arise, the cabinet becomes central. Health scares, economic crises and foreign wars ensure the cabinet's role as vital in providing political legitimacy and bolstering public confidence.

> **11** Outline the role of the following organisations and provide a specific recent example of their functioning. (AO1)   `6 marks`
>
> **The cabinet**
>
> ....

Cabinet committees

....

The Cabinet Office

....

⑫ Research the role of the cabinet secretary. (AO1)   `2 marks`

....

....

⑬ Outline and explain the nature of 'cabinet government' in the UK. (AO1, AO2 & AO3)   `10 marks`

....

....

....

....

....

....

....

....

....

....

....

Ministers

What do ministers do?

Ministers are the most influential figures within the government. Senior ministers manage departments of state, are accountable for their performance and have a seat in cabinet. Civil servants and special advisers support senior and junior ministers in the process of policy formulation.

What is individual ministerial responsibility?

Individual ministerial responsibility is the principle that government ministers are singularly responsible for their own conduct and for the performance of their departments. By convention, a minister should resign following an error or a failure to meet personal or departmental expectations.

What is collective responsibility?

Collective responsibility is a principle that underpins the effective functioning of the British government. It requires that:

- Cabinet ministers are collectively bound by government decisions.
- All members of the cabinet must support all government policy.
- If a minister disagrees privately, he or she must defend publicly.
- If a minister cannot maintain collective responsibility he or she must resign his or her cabinet post.

⑭ Complete the 'incumbent and example' section for the selected cabinet posts in the following table.

6 marks

Senior minister	Incumbent and example
Chancellor of the exchequer	George Osborne; as head of the treasury he is responsible for economic policy and delivers the budget
Home secretary	
Foreign secretary	
Secretary of state for health	
Secretary of state for international development	
Chief secretary to the Treasury	

⑮ Research and explain the reasons behind the following examples of resignations over individual responsibility.

5 marks

Year	Minister	Reason for resignation over individual responsibility
1981	Lord Carrington, foreign secretary	
1998	Peter Mandelson, Northern Ireland secretary	
2001	Estelle Morris, education secretary	
2005	David Blunkett, home secretary	
2010	David Laws, Treasury secretary	

16 Research and explain the reasons behind the following examples of resignations over collective responsibility.

Year	Minister and department	Reason for resignation over collective responsibility
2003	Robin Cook, leader of the Commons	
2003	Clare Short, international development	
2006	Tom Watson, defence	
2009	James Purnell, work and pensions	
2009	Caroline Flint, Foreign Office	

17 Outline and explain two differences between collective responsibility and individual ministerial responsibility. (AO1, AO2 & AO3)

10 marks

Write your answer on a separate sheet and keep it with your workbook for reference.

Cabinet government

How and why has cabinet government declined?

Traditionally, the cabinet was seen as the decision-making body within the core executive, with the prime minister acting merely as *primus inter pares* (first among equals). Principles of collective responsibility served to underline the collegial nature of decision making. However, in recent years several factors have led to a decline in cabinet government.

18 Explain how each of the following points might have contributed to the decline of cabinet government. (AO1, AO2 & AO3)

6 marks

The increasing complexity of government

....

....

The growth of alternative decision-making bodies

....

....

The growing status of the prime minister

....

....

....

Models of executive decision making

The decision-making process is complex and fluid. Different models exist that depend on factors such as the proximity of elections, the handling of crises and the authority or style of the prime minister.

- **Prime ministerial government**: key decisions are taken by the premier and his or her team of special advisers — or a 'kitchen cabinet' of senior figures — with cabinet ministers dealing on a departmental basis with their implementation.

- **Differentiated prime ministerial control**: in major departments of state (foreign, defence, economy) and especially matters of national security, the prime minister takes the lead but in other areas cabinet ministers are predominant.

- **Departmental government**: unless crisis intervenes, a minister's departmental expertise is unchallenged and coordinated at cabinet level by the prime minister.

Decision making in a coalition government

The creation of a coalition government had a significant impact on executive decision making. For some it heralded a **revival of collegial decision making**. For others the need for **tighter prime ministerial control** was even more apparent in the formation of the 'quad' — Cameron, Clegg, Osborne and Treasury Secretary Danny Alexander — at its apex.

19 **Explain the term *kitchen cabinet*. (AO1)**   `2 marks`

....

....

20 **Briefly explain how coalitions affect executive decision making. (AO1)**   `4 marks`

....

....

....

....

The civil service: principles and functions

Civil service principles and functions

The civil service is the administrative arm of the government, made up of many thousands of civil servants who work in government departments or agencies, engaged in policy formulation or delivering specialist services. The guiding principles of the British civil service are those of permanence (remaining in office when the government changes), anonymity (shielded from public prominence) and neutrality (serving the Crown rather than party politicians).

21 Research and explain the following civil service functions. (AO1) `4 marks`

Continuity

....

Research

....

Advice

....

Policy execution

....

Special advisers

Appointed by ministers (two per cabinet minister) and growing in number (from just five in 1990 to well over 100 in 2003), special advisers are civil servants according to the functions that they fulfil — they advise ministers and help to implement government policy — but are criticised for not being bound by traditional civil service principles.

22 Outline and explain three ways in which special advisers have undermined the traditional principles of the civil service. (AO1, AO2 & AO3) `6 marks`

....

....

....

The civil service: reform and development

23 Since the 1980s the civil service has undergone several notable reforms to its structure. Research the following changes to the structure and functioning of the civil service. (AO1)

The Fulton Report `6 marks`

....

....

The Next Steps programme and the creation of executive agencies

....

....

Reformed recruitment procedures

....

....

24 What are the main consequences of 'agencification' (or the creation of executive agencies)? (AO1)   `2 marks`

....

....

Who decides?

At the heart of the relationship between 'generalist' ministers and 'specialist' civil servants is the debate over who holds decision-making power. The constitutional position is that civil servants 'advise' while ministers 'decide', but the adversarial nature of the relationship, the lack of ministerial preparation through regular cabinet reshuffles, and the popular notion (advanced by television series such as *Yes, Minister* and *The Thick of It*) that senior civil service 'Mandarins' manipulate their 'political masters' are well established.

25 Outline an argument for and against the theory that civil servants are 'more master than servant'. (AO1, AO2 &AO3)   `4 marks`

....

....

....

....

Exam-style questions

The expansion and increased status of the Prime Minister's Office, the hundred-strong unit which directly serves the British premier, has enhanced the ability of the prime minister to oversee government strategy in a way that has made No. 10 central to the policy-making process. This centralisation of power is argued by some to have increased coordination between departments and by others to remain insufficient — when compared to the support provided for the US or German heads of state — in ensuring effective integration, policy coherence and departmental accountability.

Write your answers on a separate sheet and keep it with your workbook for reference.

26 Explain the term *Prime Minister's Office* used in the extract. (AO1)   `5 marks`

27 Using your own knowledge as well as the extract, outline and explain the principles that guide the operation of the British civil service. (AO1, AO2 & AO3)   `10 marks`

28 'Cabinet government is dead.' To what extent is this an accurate statement on executive power in the UK? (AO1, AO2 & AO3)   `25 marks`

Topic 4
Multi-level governance

Local government and democracy

The UK is a unitary state. Central government is able to make or amend any law that it wishes. However, the domination of the Westminster Parliament over the union has more recently given way to government on multiple levels. The impact and growing importance of the European Union, the devolution of power to the regions and the role played by local government are central features in the relatively new phenomenon of multi-level governance.

Local government responsibilities

The unitary nature of the UK means that local government is heavily controlled and directed by central government. However, there is also extensive coordination and provision of public services — such as schools, transport, local amenities, police and fire services, and planning — at this level.

The resources required to sustain local responsibilities are considerable and while most are funded centrally, the levy of local taxation in the form of council tax (which provides around 20% of local government revenue) is controversial and unpopular.

---

1 Briefly explain the term *multi-level governance*. (AO1)   `2 marks`

....

....

2 Outline and explain one advantage and one disadvantage of *local government*. (AO1)   `2 marks`

....

....

3 Research and explain at least two reasons why *council tax* is considered to be controversial and unpopular. (AO1)   `3 marks`

....

....

....

Is local democracy in decline?

Local democracy is the principle that decisions should be taken as closely as possible to the people affected by them. This serves to ensure that they are in line with local wishes and responsive to them. Evidence that local democracy is in decline includes:

- **poor turnout** at local elections (usually under 40%), with voting following national rather than local issues
- **lack of financial autonomy** with central government controlling and dictating local spending
- **the outsourcing of public services** to private bodies, e.g. refuse collection, housing associations, academy chains

4 Research and outline three arguments supporting the 'renewal' of local democracy. (AO1) `3 marks`

....

....

....

Devolution in the UK

What is devolution?

Devolution is the transfer of power from central government to subordinate levels of government — regions, cities and some local authorities. The process of devolution began in 1997 and the next 2 years saw the creation of the Scottish Parliament, the Welsh Assembly, the Northern Ireland Assembly and the Greater London Authority.

A significant element of the process of devolution involves the election of representatives to carry out key responsibilities at a level that is closer to those affected. Elected representatives in Wales and Scotland have responsibilities over a large number of areas such as agriculture, education, health and transport.

5 Research and briefly explain how *legislative* and *administrative devolution* differed between Scotland and Wales. (AO1) `2 marks`

....

....

....

6 What are *primary legislative powers*? Provide examples. (AO1) `3 marks`

....

....

....

How has devolution affected relations between the centre and the regions?

One of the key reasons that the process of devolution in 1997 sparked opposition and controversy was that it seemed to undermine the fundamental principles of the UK's unitary state.

- On a theoretical level, Parliament remains sovereign and powers are merely delegated. The UK is not federal, and sovereignty is not constitutionally divided between different elements of the state. The suspension of the Northern Ireland Assembly when power-sharing arrangements broke down (2002–07) illustrates Parliament's continued authority.

- On a practical level, the entrenchment of the devolved bodies by popular referendum means that they cannot simply be dissolved. This, coupled with further European integration, has contributed to a process seen as 'federalism by stealth' (or 'quasi-federalism') with central government power draining in each direction.

7 Why is the UK referred to as being a *unitary state*? (AO1)   `2 marks`

....

....

8 Outline two arguments in support of the view that 'the UK is federalist in all
but name'. (AO1, AO2 & AO3)   `10 marks`

....

....

....

....

....

....

....

....

Regional government: Scotland and Wales

Evaluating the Scottish Parliament

The Scottish Parliament was created in 1999 following the success of the 'Yes' vote (in support of both devolution and tax-varying powers) in the 1997 referendum. The parliament took control of key areas of domestic policy and immediately set about abolishing university top-up fees and enhancing free nursing care for the elderly.

9 Research and explain:

The significance of the West Lothian Question (AO1, AO2 & AO3)   `3 marks`

....

....

Calls for Scottish independence (AO1)   `2 marks`

....

....

Evaluating the Welsh Assembly

Following a narrow 'Yes' vote in the 1997 referendum (by 50.3% on a 50.1% turnout), the Welsh Assembly was created in 1999. Its secondary legislative powers meant that it could either recommend legislation to Westminster or determine the implementation of Westminster legislation but could not legislate in its own right.

10 Research and explain:

Asymmetrical devolution (AO1, AO2 & AO3)   `3 marks`

....

....

....

Wales' appetite for enhanced powers (AO1)   `2 marks`

....

....

The European Union

The UK's relationship with the European Union has been complex and controversial. Membership has had an impact on all aspects of the UK's politics and public policy. It has undermined long-standing constitutional principles and divided parties and public opinion. For some, the freedom of movement and trade and the settled relationships that exist between the member states is a price worth paying for the expensive bureaucracies of the EU's supranational institutions.

An integration timeline

The EU has its origins in the European Coal and Steel Community formed in 1952 between France, Germany and Italy. In the following decades it steadily expanded its membership and responsibilities until the UK joined the European Economic Community in January 1973.

11 Define the term *qualified majority voting*. What are its implications? (AO1)   `3 marks`

....

....

....

12 What does *supranational* mean? Explain with examples. (AO1)   `2 marks`

....

....

13 Outline and explain two ways that *EU membership has affected the UK's political systems.* (AO1, AO2 & AO3)   `4 marks`

Parliamentary sovereignty

....

....

The UK judicial system

....

....

14 Research and explain the implications of the key milestones in the following table. Try to think of the way that membership has affected the UK's institutions and political processes.

6 marks

Selected milestones	Significance
Single European Act, 1986	The establishment of an internal market within the EU allowing free movement of goods and workers. Introduction of Qualified Majority Voting (QMV)
Maastricht Treaty, 1992	
Treaty of Amsterdam, 1997	
Treaty of Nice, 2001	
Enlargement to 25 member states, 2004	
European Constitution, 2004	
Lisbon Treaty, 2007	

Composition and functions

- The **European Commission** is the 'executive' of the EU, made up of 27 commissioners (one from each state) and a president. It proposes legislation and attempts to ensure that the provisions of the various treaties are upheld.
- The **Council** (formerly the Council of Ministers) is made up of ministers of the 27 member states and is the decision-making body of the EU. Key decisions are reached by unanimous vote and lesser ones by QMV.

- The **European Council** (known as the European Summit) is the forum for heads of state, foreign secretaries and commissioners to determine the direction of the EU.
- The **European Parliament** is made up of 736 MEPs elected from member states every 5 years. Its primary roles are to scrutinise the EU budget and the European Commission itself.
- The **European Court of Justice** administers and adjudicates on EU law. Made up of 27 judges (one from each member state) it is able to strike down domestic laws where they conflict with EU law.

15 Explain the role of the *European Council*. (AO1)

2 marks

....

....